Bicycles, Airships and Things that *Go!*

By Bernie McAllister

Illustrated by John Aardema

Kids Future Press

London • Seattle

Thanks to 20th century children's writers and illustrators Richard Scarry, Virginia Lee Burton, and Robert McCloskey for inspiring our 21st century road trip.

Learn more about the designers and engineers who inspired us on page 31.

Kids Future Press

Bicycles, Airships and Things that Go

© Bernie McAllister and John Aardema 2015 Moral rights asserted.
Designed by Sandra Perry

First published in 2015 by Kids Future Press.

ISBN 978-0-9916255-0-5

This family is going on a trip. Why don't you come along with Tilly and Taylor and their mom and dad? Here's how it all started…

Mom's an inventor and she's created a suit covered in lights. The suit makes night-time activities look amazing. The children see Brooke Frost snowboarding in it.

"That is so cool!" cries Taylor. "Wow," says Tilly. "I'd love to wear it." Mom surprises them by asking if they'd like to visit the town of Sunnyside with her and Dad. "We could all go and deliver this suit to the science center. They'll put it in a show about high-tech clothing."

Dad

Tilly

Taylor

Mom

LED light suit

Solar panel bag

3

Beehive

Solar panels

Wall garden

Street tree

Solar power
streetlight

Recycle and
compost bins

Bike parking

Electric
car

Open paving
(absorbs water)

4

Roof garden

Wind turbines

It looks like the children are excited about the trip—they're literally shouting from the rooftop. They live here in Garden City. I wonder how they'll travel to Sunnyside.

Hey! Who are those two peeking out from the alley?

Solar Hornet

This is the solar hornet, discovered in 2010. He's the only animal with built-in solar cells to generate energy from sunlight. He turns up on every page, so see if you can spot him.

Solar lounger

Street trees

Stacking electric cars

5

They're off! Dad takes the family bags on his cargo bike. Mom and the children ride on their own bikes. Which bike would you like to try?

Front-load freight bike

Tandem bike

Spies

Electric car

There are spies who want that light suit—those two from the alley. Look at them in their electric car.

BMX bikes

Recumbent bike with trailer

Recycle & compost bins

compost

Cargo bike

Oh no...

6

Over-loaded bike

Bike café

Unicycle

Kids bikes

Fold-up bike

Family commuter bike

...where's the right place for those banana peels?

It's time to park the bikes. Mom and Dad spot some parking places while the kids look at the garden. Some of it grows on the wall outside, but there's also a big greenhouse.

Bike parking garage

City gardeners

8

And what about those two spies? They have to plug in their electric car so it will be ready to drive when they get back. By the way, where's that solar hornet?

Greenhouse (indoor urban farm)

Wind Turbine

Wall garden

Open paving (absorbs water)

Rain Barrel

Charging electric cars

9

City roof gardens

Solar panels

10

The family's taking the airship to Sunnyside. The airship is filled with gas that's lighter than air, so it floats like a birthday balloon.

Those spies are late. Are they going to get on board?

Airship

Playground

Arboretum

Wind turbine farm

Wave energy machines

The airship flies over the sea. "Wow, it's really blowing—look at those wind turbines go!" says Dad. "Maybe the wind will make the airship go faster!" Taylor exclaims.

Dad's a wind turbine mechanic and he spots some of his friends at work. When they see him he waves. Can you see his friends waving?

Do solar hornets like wind and sea?

Towing kite

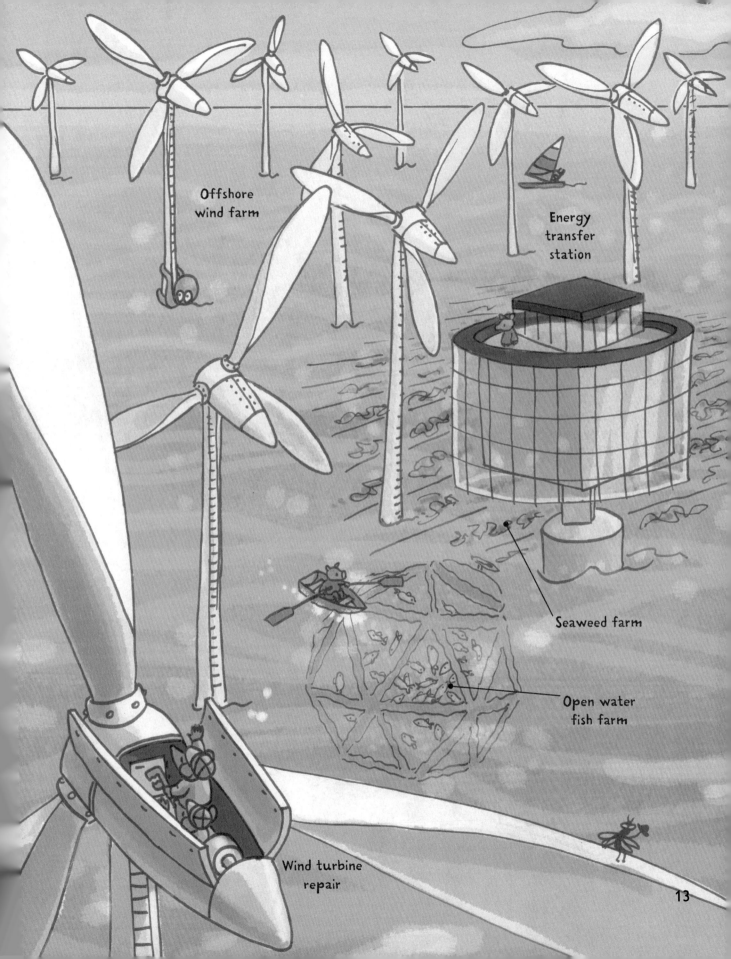

Offshore
wind farm

Energy
transfer
station

Seaweed farm

Open water
fish farm

Wind turbine
repair

13

Up in the airship, Dad's getting a snack with the children.
Mom wants to take some pictures, but her battery has run
out. Luckily she can plug her camera in to her solar bag.

Dad's left the package on the table. Mom's nearby but
she's not looking. Phew! Her camera scares off the spies
just as they make their move. I wonder if she's accidentally
snapped a picture of them.

15

Hillside
solar farm

Sand boarding

16

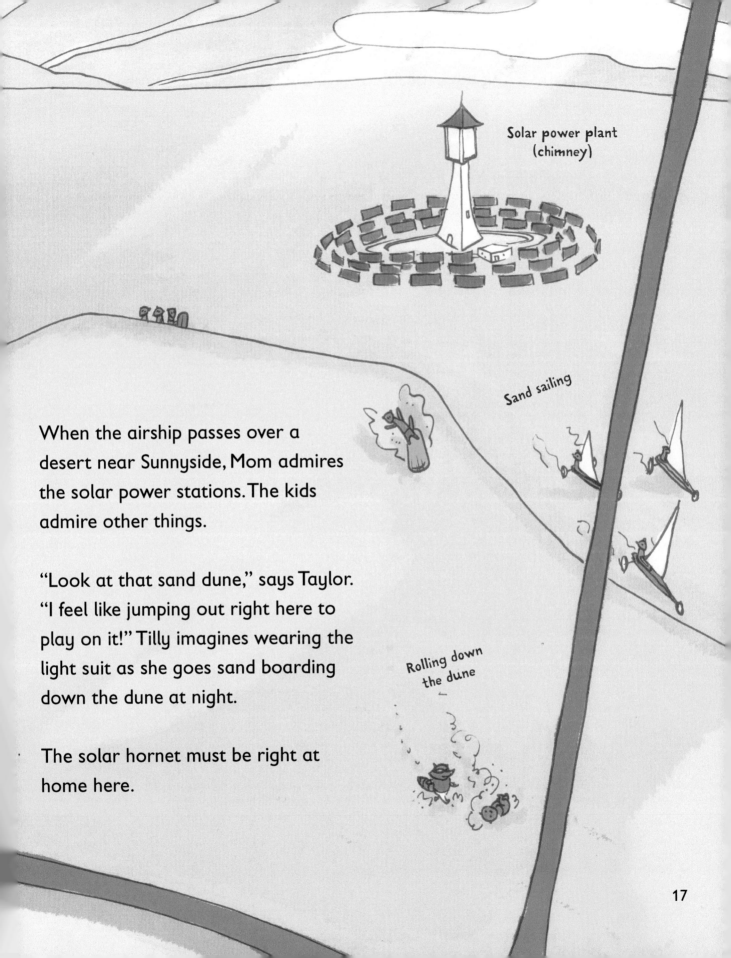

Solar power plant
(chimney)

Sand sailing

Rolling down
the dune

When the airship passes over a desert near Sunnyside, Mom admires the solar power stations. The kids admire other things.

"Look at that sand dune," says Taylor. "I feel like jumping out right here to play on it!" Tilly imagines wearing the light suit as she goes sand boarding down the dune at night.

The solar hornet must be right at home here.

The airship lands in Sunnyside. Look at that spy! He's made a grab for the package, but he tripped on a bicycle pump.

Low energy building

Bus-top garden

Solar power streetlight

Bike bus

Station scooter

Mom takes the bags and the package over to the science center in a cargo scooter. It's a station scooter, so she borrows it from the station and returns it later.

Dad and the children are about to ride the bus when they see the *bike bus* coming.

The children beg Dad to let them ride it. They say, "Please, *please!*" He decides they can get on and join the other peddlers.

Airship

Solar panels

AIRSHIP

Motorcycles

Electric cars

Bike parking

At the science center Mom and Tilly hand over the package to the director. The director's given them a cake to take home.

Mummies

Where are those spies now? All the fun exhibits distract them. They don't know that Mom has a different package now. Will they chase the wrong package all the way back to Garden City?

SCIENCE CENTER

Water play area

Dinosaur skeleton

Geometry play area

Recycle & compost bins

The family's got time to look around Sunnyside. First stop is the skate park. Tilly's pretty good at it! No wonder she wanted to wear the light suit. Look at her jump.

Mom and Dad try dancing on the tiles at Echo Plaza. Their steps make a pattern that shows up on the wall of a nearby building.

Skateboard park

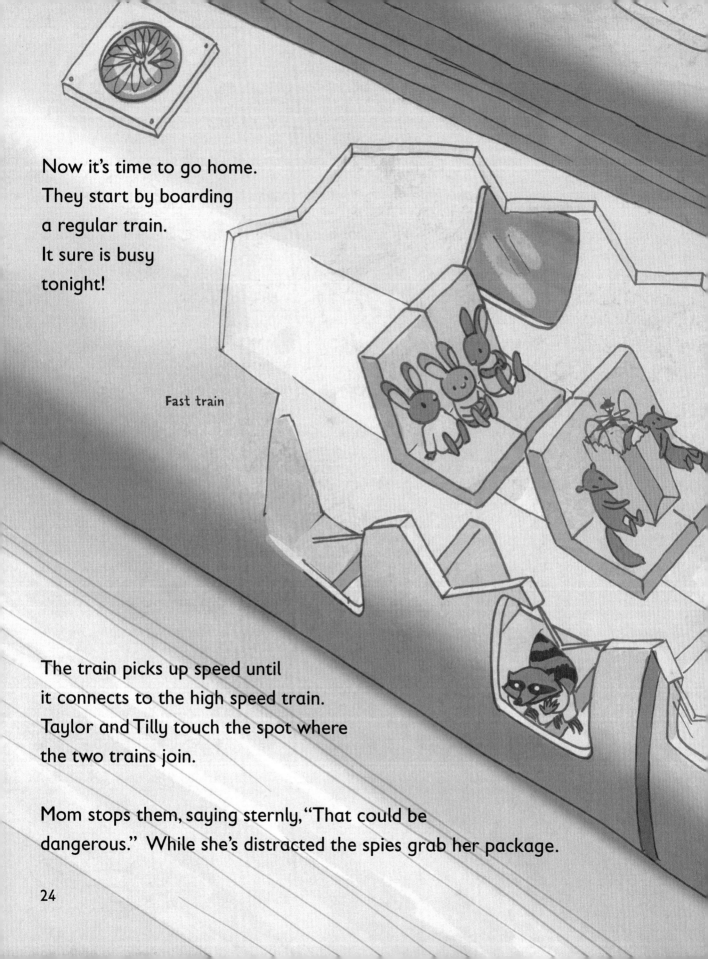

Now it's time to go home.
They start by boarding
a regular train.
It sure is busy
tonight!

Fast train

The train picks up speed until
it connects to the high speed train.
Taylor and Tilly touch the spot where
the two trains join.

Mom stops them, saying sternly, "That could be
dangerous." While she's distracted the spies grab her package.

24

Slow train

Train
connector

Solar
panels

On the ferry from the train station, the children stand at the back and look at the boat's wake. Taylor boasts about swimming as fast as the boat.

The spies have to get home too, and they're still following Mom and the family. They're trying to hide under the solar panels, but it doesn't look very comfortable.

Finally Mom notices them. She recognizes them from Garden City's Science *Museum*, a rival of the Science *Center* in Sunnyside where they just delivered the suit. "Hello! What are you doing up there?" she calls.

Look at those folks with the origami kayaks—they fold up so small!

Folding kayak

Getting home, the family stops at the local park. The children make balloon cars. How do those cars move? I think Taylor and Tilly's car is winning!

That playground looks really familiar. Can you see what it's made of?

Uh oh, Mom discovers her package is missing.

Playground

Balloon cars

At home Dad asks, "What was your favorite part of the trip?" Tilly says hers was the skate park in Sunnyside. Taylor says his was the science center. Mom says hers was the airship ride and she shows her pictures.

When they see the picture from inside the airship, Mom says, "Hey, it's that guy from the Science Museum here in Garden City—he must be the one who took the package." Tilly adds, "He probably wanted that light suit, not a cake!" Everyone laughs and Dad brings out a cake he made earlier.

Hanging beds

Dad lowers the kids' beds down from the ceiling
and tells them, "No swinging or jumping tonight.
You've had a big day and it's time to sleep."
Good night to you too, solar hornet.

Sources that inspired this book

Find internet links for these and other sources at www.kidsfuturepress.com. **Page 3**: LED light suit inspired by photographer Jacob Sutton's concept, designed by John Spatcher, worn by snowboarder William Hughes. **Page 4-5**: Neighborhood inspired by living streets and ecodistricts, as championed by Portland's Ecodistricts organization. MIT's proposed stackable 'city cars' inspire our row of electric vehicles. MIT's Sheila Kennedy and students made the solar lounger. The solar hornet is alone in the animal kingdom in generating electricity from the sun's light; tissues with yellow pigment trap light, while tissues with brown pigments generate electricity. **Page 6-7**: The wide range of bicycles available today inspires our scene. **Page 8-9**: Bike parking inspired by Amsterdam Centraal Station. Vertical gardens inspired by the work of Patrick Blanc and urban agriculturists. Electric vehicle charging is becoming available in many cities. **Page 10-11**: Although passenger airships may be futuristic, companies such as Hybrid Air Vehicles and Aeros are developing cargo and military airships. **Page 12-13**: German company SkySails makes automated towing kites and wind propulsion systems for ships. Vattenfall's Lillgrund, with 48 turbines operational since 2007, inspires our transformer station and wind farm. **Page 16-17**: Solar power plants exist in both circular "chimneys" and field-like "farms." Belgian energy firm Enfinity's facility in Les Mées, France inspired our hillside farm. **Page 18-19**: Bike buses inspired by Dutch company Tolkamp Metaalspecials and Boston-based Busycle (Heather Clark and Matthew Mazzotta). The angled glass building is based on top U.S. energy-efficient Federal Center South Building 1202 by ZGF Architects with landscape by SiteWorkshop. Enviro-award winning Kuggen office building (Gothenburg, Sweden) inspired the saw-tooth facade. Designers Marc Grañén and Marco Castro (Bus Roots), in Spanish and U.S. cities, inspired the garden-top bus. **Page 22-23**: Electroland's "Enteractive" (by Cameron McNall and Damon Seeley) inspired the interactive light plaza; Tilly's skateboarding is inspired by female skaters including Lucy Adams, Lacey Baker, Leticia Bufoni, Amy Caron, Marisa Dal Santo, and Vanessa Torres. **Page 24-25**: Paul Priestman conceptualized a network of local trams that dock with high-speed trains at the city periphery to avoid waiting at station platforms. **Page 26-27**: Ferry inspired by Australian Solar Sailor ferries and by the world's largest 100% solar-powered boat, Planet Solar's Tûranor, by Raphaël Domjan and Immo Stroeher. Oru by Anton Willis inspires the folding kayak. **Page 28-29**: The playground made from wind turbine rotors is inspired by the Wikado playground (2008) by Jeroen Bergsma, Césare Peeren, and Jos de Krieger of Dutch firm Superuse Studios. Compost bins are inspired by Italy's Metalsistem SUPERINOX outdoor furniture.

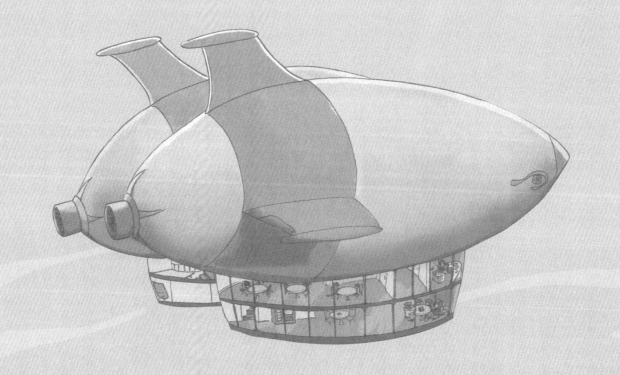

41167061R00020

Made in the USA
San Bernardino, CA
06 November 2016